Spelling, Punctuation & Grammar Made Easy

Author Claire White
Consultant Amy O'Connor

LONDON • NEW YORK • MELBOURNE • MUNICH • DELHI

Certificate

Congratulations to

....
(write your name here)

for successfully finishing this book.

GOOD JOB!

You're a star.

AGES 5-7

Key Stage 1

Date

....

 Penguin Random House

Editors Jolyon Goddard, Nandini Gupta
Art Editor Rashika Kachroo
Assistant Art Editor Radhika Kapoor
Managing Editor Soma B. Chowdhury
Managing Art Editors Richard Czapnik, Ahlawat Gunjan
Senior Producer, Pre-Production Ben Marcus
Producer Christine Ni
DTP Designer Anita Yadav

First published in Great Britain in 2015 by
Dorling Kindersley Limited
80 Strand, London WC2R 0RL

Copyright © 2015 Dorling Kindersley Limited
A Penguin Random House Company
10 9 8 7 6 5 4 3 2 1
001—270529—Jan/2015

A CIP catalogue record for this book
is available from the British Library.
ISBN 978-0-2411-8271-0

Printed and bound in China by L. Rex Printing Co. Ltd.

All images © Dorling Kindersley Limited
For further information see: www.dkimages.com

A WORLD OF IDEAS:
SEE ALL THERE IS TO KNOW

Contents

This chart lists all of the topics in the book. When you complete each page, stick a star in the correct box. When you have finished the book, sign and date the certificate.

FACTS

Each letter in the **alphabet** has two forms: a **capital**, or upper-case, letter and a **small**, or lower-case, letter.

Match the capital letters to their small letters. Say the letters as you match them. The first one has been done for you.

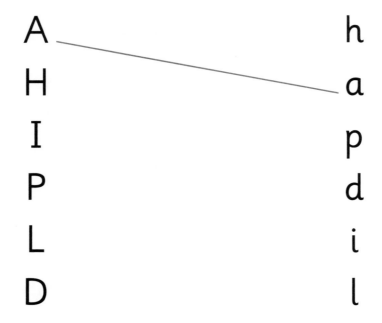

A   h

H   a

I   p

P   d

L   i

D   l

Eric has made a list of places that he would like to visit during his trip to London. He has missed out the capital letters while writing the names. Help him pick the correct capital letter from the box below.

L   B   E   T

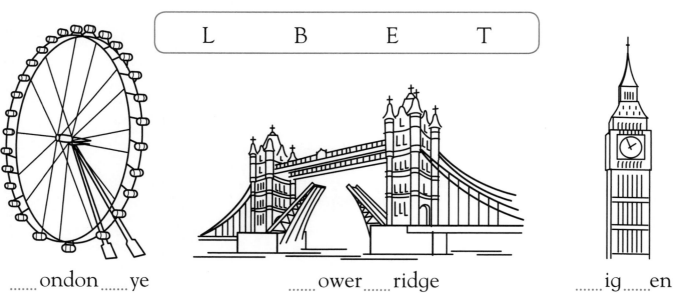

......ondon ......ye   ......ower ......ridge   ......ig ......en

The alphabet is the set of **letters** we use in our writing.
The English alphabet starts with **Aa** and ends with **Zz**.

Practise saying the letters of the alphabet in order.

a	b	c	d	e	f	g	h	i	j	k	l	m
n	o	p	q	r	s	t	u	v	w	x	y	z

Look at the sets of letters below. Using the table above, put each set in the correct alphabetical order. The first one has been done for you.

bcadfe .... abcdef ....

dhnyzx ....

abueit ....

zoltqs ....

hnewcv ....

lopdef ....

ksnmfl ....

jgilad ....

ywstxi ....

FACTS

It is important to leave a **finger space** between each **word** in a **sentence**, so your writing is easy to read and understand.

The aliens from the planet Zognog have written some sentences. In alien language, however, there are no spaces between the words. So it can be very difficult to read their sentences. In each sentence, draw a line where you think the finger spaces should appear. We have done the first one for you.

I|live|on|the|Moon.

Todayismybirthday.

Threeeyesarebetterthantwo!

IamBo-Bo.

MyfriendiscalledBee-Bee.

Mycatissmall.

You should always use a **capital letter** for the names of people, places, days of the week and the personal pronoun **I**.

Finley has made a list of the friends he wants to invite to his birthday party. However, he has forgotten to write the capital letter at the start of their names. Make a new list to show Finley the correct way to write the names.

Guest list

tom

jack

zoe

imogen

harry

daisy

isobel

eloise

joshua

Guest list

....

....

....

....

....

....

....

....

....

FACTS

Personal pronouns are the small words you can use instead of a **noun** when it is already clear what or whom you are talking about. They include the words **she**, **it**, **you** and **I**. The personal pronoun **I** should always be written in its capital form.

Rebecca has written some sentences about her birthday, but she has forgotten to use capital letters. Write her sentences again, but this time with capital letters in the correct places. **Remember**: names of people and places begin with capital letters.

i will be six.

....

i am having a party.

....

at my party, i would like games.

....

i have invited my best friend sam.

....

my party will be in london.

....

i have been looking forward to my birthday party.

....

There are seven days in a week. The weekend has two days, which both start with the capital letter **S**.

Bee-Bee and his friends have a spaceship for each day of the week. Unfortunately, Bee-Bee has got in a muddle when labelling the spaceships. Help him by writing the days of the week correctly on each spaceship.

Monday   Tuesday

Wednesday   Thursday   Friday

Saturday   Sunday

unSady

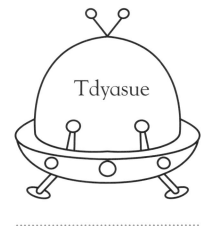

Tdyasue

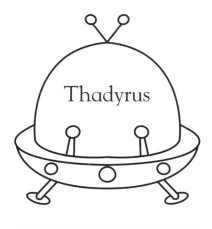

Thadyrus

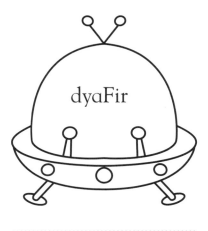

dyaFir

turSayad

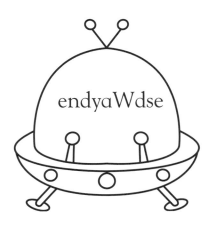

endyaWdse

yadonM

Punctuation marks make your writing easier to understand and read. They also help you add expression and know when to change the tone of your voice when reading aloud.

Punctuation mark	What it is called	Why it is used
.	full stop	It shows where a sentence ends.
,	comma	It shows a pause between parts of a sentence or separates items in a list.
!	exclamation mark	It shows a strong reaction or feeling.
?	question mark	It shows that a sentence is a question. It goes at the end of the question.
,	apostrophe	It shows where a letter is missing in contractions, such as **wasn't** or **don't**.

Each sentence below is missing a punctuation mark at the end. Help end the sentences by deciding which punctuation mark fits best. Is it a full stop, a question mark or an exclamation mark?

The boy fell into the mud......

The door shut with a BANG......

What is your name......

Why are you laughing.....

The elephant was having a shower.....

A simple sentence ends with a **full stop**; a **question** ends with a **question mark**; and an **exclamation mark** shows excitement.

Maisie the Monster isn't very good at using punctuation. Look at the letter she has written to Marlon and underline the letters that should be capital letters. Then, using the table on the opposite page, add the missing punctuation marks where necessary.

246 maddison close
chichester
west sussex
england

dear marlon

thank you for the letter i ve enjoyed reading all about what you have been doing i have also been cooking my favourite cake is chocolate what is your favourite type of cake it has been raining here since tuesday and i am fed up with not being able to go outside and play i do like jumping in muddy puddles just like you do splish splash splosh

i hope to see you soon

love
maisie

Commas

In a sentence, **commas** can be used to separate words in a list. Using commas makes the list easier to read as it allows you to take a short breath between reading each word.

Look at the sentences below and add the commas in the correct places. **Remember**: we do not use a comma before the word **and** in a list.

We saw some giraffes penguins tigers and red pandas at the zoo.

Imogen likes pizza pasta curry and cake.

My friend Zoe has two cats a fish two chickens and a dog.

A police officer needs a notebook a pencil and a pair of handcuffs.

Now make a list of your own, such as your pets or favourite sports, putting the commas in the correct places.

....

....

....

When **nouns** are **singular**, there is just one of them, such as **a house**. When nouns are **plural**, there are more than one of them, such as **five foxes**. In English, we usually create the plural by adding **s** to the end. However, sometimes we add **es**. Adding **es** happens most often when the singular word ends with **s**, **ss**, **x**, **ch** or **sh**.

Circle the correct plural word for each of the singular words below.

dog   dogs or doges

flower   floweres or flowers

church   churches or churchs

brush   brushs or brushes

car   cars or cares

box   boxes or boxs

Now see if you can think of some singular words on your own and their plurals.

For **singular nouns** that end in **f** or **fe**, there are two rules to remember when making them **plural**.

If the word ends in a single **f**, you usually change **f** to **v** and add **es**.

For example:

scarf

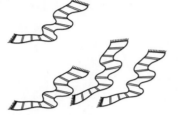

scarves

If the word ends in **fe**, change **fe** to **ves**.

For example:

wife

wives

Read the sentences below carefully and circle the irregular plurals.

There was one wolf.
Now there are lots of wolves.

There was one knife on the table.
Now there are lots of knives on the table.

There was once an elf.
All his friends were elves, too.

The cake has been cut in half, making two halves.

The letters **ing** are a common ending, or **suffix**, to words.
If the **root word** has a short **vowel** sound and more than one
consonant after it, then just add **ing**.

Add **ing** to each word to make an action word.
The first one has been done for you.

Root word		Suffix		
stand	+	ing	=	standing
stick	+	ing	=	....
back	+	ing	=	....
jump	+	ing	=	....
bless	+	ing	=	....
rock	+	ing	=	....
lift	+	ing	=	....

If a **root word** has a short **vowel** with only one consonant after it, then you must **double** the consonant when adding **ing**.

Add **ing** to each word to complete the word sums.
The first one has been done for you.

Root word		Suffix		
skip	+	ing	=	skipping

beg	+	ing	=	....
hit	+	ing	=	....

hug	+	ing	=	....
put	+	ing	=	....
lap	+	ing	=	....

nod	+	ing	=	....
sit	+	ing	=	....

FACTS

A **noun** names a person, a place or a thing. A **common noun** is a general name for something, such as **dog** or **house**. A **proper noun** names a specific person or place, such as **Oliver** or **Cornwall**.

On the washing line, there are many pairs of trousers.
Colour the trousers that have a noun written on them.

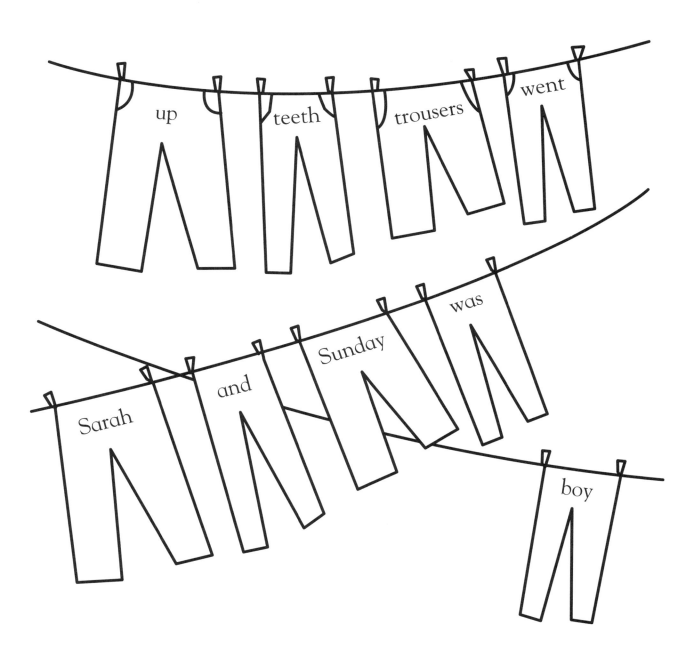

When we want to add description to a noun, such as **book**, we can use adjectives or groups of words that give extra information about the noun. For example: **the red book, an old, dusty book** and **my favourite book on the shelf** are all **expanded noun phrases** describing the noun **book**.

Read the poem below and then circle the expanded noun phrases. The first one has been done for you.

(Bo-Bo the crazy alien) went one day

To a distant planet far away.

With him went his best friend Zag

And they packed a jumbo travelling bag.

Use alliteration to expand the information about each of these nouns. You can choose words from the box below to help you.

| silly | slippery | setting | slimy | shining | smelly |

.... socks

.... sun

.... snail

.... sausage

FACTS

A **collective noun** is a word that names a group of people, places or things; for example: a **pack** of wolves.

Pick a collective noun from the box below. What group of things does it describe? Write the word you chose on the correct dotted line. Then draw that group. The first one has been done for you.

crowd	herd	school	swarm	
flock	colony	fleet		pride

bees .... swarm	people ....
cows	birds ....
fish	lions ....
bats	ships ....

FACTS

> **Pronouns** are words that can take the place of nouns in a sentence. Examples include **she**, **you**, **my** and **their**.

Circle the pronoun in each sentence.

The dog ate my shoe.

They are all going to the park.

Eleanor wore her best dress.

Where are you going?

We are going on holiday.

I like to eat chocolate.

He bought some new trainers.

Write three sentences of your own that include pronouns.

....

....

....

A **homophone** is a word that is pronounced the same as another word but has a different meaning and spelling, such as **which** and **witch**.

Draw lines joining the phones that have homophones on their screens. The first one has been done for you.

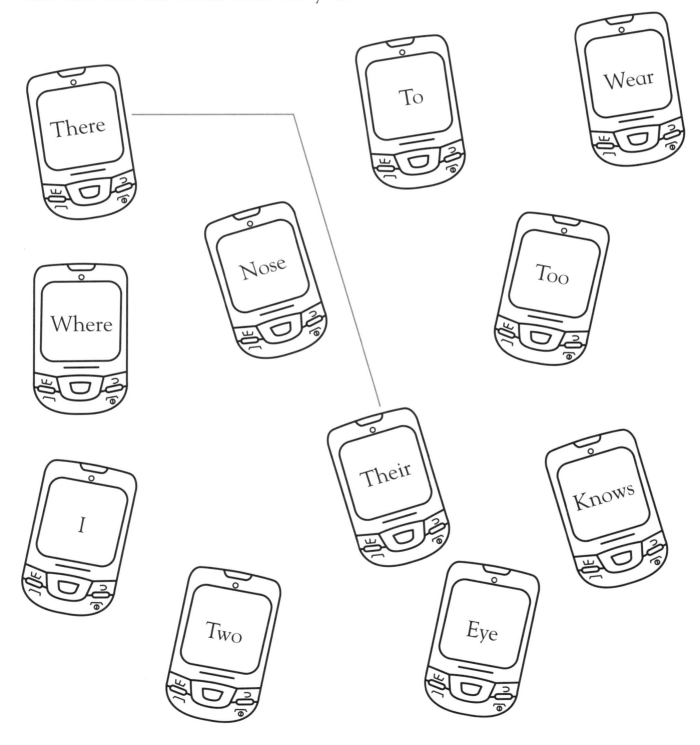

Near homophones are words that sound similar but aren't pronounced exactly the same, such as **chair** and **cheer**.

In the table below, circle the homophones and put a cross through the near homophones.

been/bin	would/wood
hair/hare	bought/brought
caught/cot	four/for

Now in each of these sentences, choose the correct homophone and circle it.

They're/their/there going to have a party at they're/their/there house and everyone will be they're/their/there.

I can't decide where/wear I will where/wear my new dress.

As I got closer to the beach, I could see/sea the see/sea.

An **adjective** is a describing word, such as **hot** or **cold**. Adjectives add detail to nouns and can make writing more interesting.

Complete these descriptions by using the correct adjective for each picture. The first one has been done for you.

The teddy bear is   soft   .

The cat is   .

The alien is   .

The necklace is   .

The monster is   .

The flower is   .

My friend is   .

★ Verbs

Verbs are **doing** words. Verbs can express a physical action, as in to **swim**, **write** or **climb**; a mental action, as in to **think**, **guess** or **consider**; or a state of being, as in to **be**, **exist** or **appear**.

The sentences on this page are missing verbs. Fill them in by choosing verbs from the word box below. You can use the same verb more than once. The first one has been done for you.

| dance | jumps | see | smile | fly | sings | plays |

The cat ...plays... the guitar.

The cow .... over the moon.

It was silly of the dog to .... on the table.

Rita .... with joy.

William will .... at the carnival.

When the bird ...., it makes me ....

Samuel .... while Arthur .... the piano.

They wanted to .... who could .... the farthest.

Verbs can describe what happened in the past, what is happening in the present (now) and what will happen in the future.

Past tense	Present tense	Future tense
The event has already happened.	The event is happening now.	The event is going to happen.

Read the sentences below and draw a line between each one and one of the cars. Past-tense sentences go to the vintage car, present-tense sentences go to the modern car and future-tense sentences go to the car of the future.

Henry is doing his
school work.

I am going to become
a teacher one day.

I went to the park last week.

John screamed when he
saw the spider.

At the display, the fireworks
will go bang!

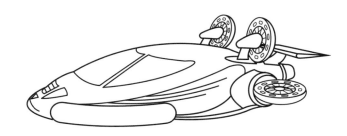

Kate lives in a town.

FACTS

Verbs in the **past tense** name an action that has already happened. Some verbs can be changed to the past tense by adding **ed** to the end.

Read the letter Marlon the Monster has written to his friend Maisie. Pick the correct verbs from the box below to fill in the blanks.

baked	jumped	tasted	skipped
played	helped	walked	

Dear Maisie,

I had a busy day yesterday! First, my mum and I .... a cake. It .... really nice. Then my dad and I went outside and I .... in muddy puddles, which was great fun! After that, as we .... home, it started to rain hard. So we put the umbrella up and .... the rest of the way. When we got home, we .... a game. Finally, I .... my mum make tea.

I hope you've had a good day, too!

Love,
Marlon
xxx

> Verbs in the **present tense** name an action that is happening now.

Marlon is in a muddle with his present-tense verbs. Help him complete his sentences by choosing the correct verb from the box below.

drinks	likes	write	buy	send	see	fly

The pink monster .... to eat sweets.

Maisie .... milk in the morning.

I can .... all my monster friends.

I .... letters every day.

We .... our own monster snacks.

I .... in my diary daily.

They .... really high.

Can you write two more sentences with present-tense verbs?

....

....

★ Future tense

We use the **future tense** when an action has not already happened, nor is happening now, but will happen later.

Complete each sentence by choosing the correct verb from the box below. **Remember**: in the future tense, verbs are usually paired with **will** or **shall**.

| ride | help | go | meet | play | take | invite |

Joan .... to college next month.

He .... Mum cook dinner next week.

I .... you at the park after school.

We .... on the swings in the park.

William .... his dog with him to the park.

George .... Esther to his sister's wedding.

Henry .... his scooter to school tomorrow.

We can make longer sentences from simple sentences by using a **connective**. A connective is a word that joins two simple sentences together to make one long sentence. Two very common connectives are **and** and **but**. We use **and** when we expect the second part of a sentence to follow the first part. We use **but** when we do not expect the second part to follow the first part.

Make these pairs of short sentences into one longer sentence by choosing the connective word (**and** or **but**) that fits best. Write the new extended sentence below each pair. Add a comma before **but**, do not add it before **and**.

It was a lovely day. We enjoyed our picnic.

....

It was getting dark. Zoe wasn't frightened.

....

Ethan and Rowan got up late. They got to school on time.

....

The baby giggled. She smiled at me.

....

I bumped my head. It didn't hurt.

....

Alena got a new dress. She wore her old one.

....

A **contraction** is a shortened form of one or two words. In a contraction, an **apostrophe** takes the place of the missing letter or letters. For example: **I am** ➞ **I'm** and **you are** ➞ **you're**.

Help Elfed, the contraction wizard, choose the correct potion to make the right contractions. Colour the two bottles of potion the wizard needs to make the word on the cauldron.

Can you think of any other contractions?

....

FACTS

There are lots of different types of **sentence**, both in spoken and written language. Using a variety of sentences will make your conversations and writing much more interesting. There are four different types of sentence, shown here below each person.

Look at the sentences below and write which type of sentence they are, using the words in the box.

statement	exclamation	question	command

What have you done at school today? ....

Watch out! ....

The girl is singing. ....

What a huge spider! ....

Please be quiet. ....

How old are you? ....

It is important to learn how to spell words, especially as many common words are not pronounced exactly as they are spelled.

Read each column of these very common words.
Next, cover the words up one by one and write them down on the dotted lines.

again	....	little	....
all	....	much	....
over	....	what	....
took	....	him	....
very	....	open	....
want	....	everyone	....
yes	....	sister	....
some	....	our	....
there	....	people	....
down	....	up	....
school	....	because	....
just	....	come	....

Answer section with parents' notes

Key Stage 1
Ages 5–7

This eight-page section provides answers and explanatory notes to all the activities in this book, enabling you to assess your child's work.

Work through each page together and ensure that your child understands each task. Point out any mistakes your child makes and correct any spelling errors. (Your child should use the handwriting style taught at his or her school.) In addition to making corrections, it is very important to praise your child's efforts and achievements.

At the end of this section, there is a glossary that includes all of the key terms covered in this book.

★ The alphabet

Each letter in the **alphabet** has two forms: a **capital**, or upper-case, letter and a **small**, or lower-case, letter.

Match the capital letters to their small letters. Say the letters as you match them. The first one has been done for you.

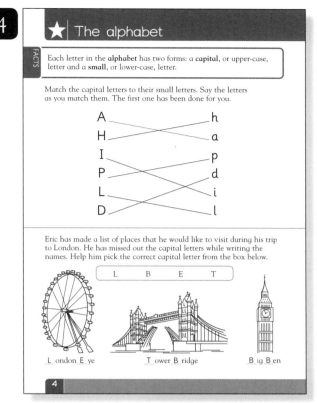

Eric has made a list of places that he would like to visit during his trip to London. He has missed out the capital letters while writing the names. Help him pick the correct capital letter from the box below.

L   B   E   T

L ondon E ye   T ower B ridge   B ig B en

Help your child remember the order of the letters in the alphabet by asking questions such as "Which letter comes straight after B?" and "Name a letter in the alphabet that comes after S."

Alphabetical order ★

The alphabet is the set of **letters** we use in our writing. The English alphabet starts with **Aa** and ends with **Zz**.

Practise saying the letters of the alphabet in order.

a b c d e f g h i j k l m
n o p q r s t u v w x y z

Look at the sets of letters below. Using the table above, put each set in the correct alphabetical order. The first one has been done for you.

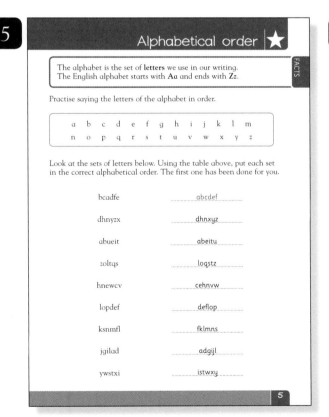

bcadfe   abcdef

dhnyzx   dhnxyz

abueit   abeitu

zoltqs   loqstz

hnewcv   cehnvw

lopdef   deflop

ksnmfl   fklmns

jgilad   adgijl

ywstxi   istwxy

You can help your child practise his or her knowledge of alphabetical order when you are teaching him or her how to use a dictionary. Challenge your child by asking him or her to look up the definition of a given word.

★ Finger spaces

It is important to leave a **finger space** between each **word** in a **sentence**, so your writing is easy to read and understand.

The aliens from the planet Zognog have written some sentences. In alien language, however, there are no spaces between the words. So it can be very difficult to read their sentences. In each sentence, draw a line where you think the finger spaces should appear. We have done the first one for you.

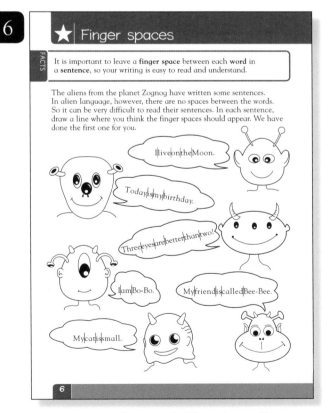

I live on the Moon.

Today is my birthday.

Three eyes are better than two!

I am Bo-Bo.

My friend is called Bee-Bee.

My cat is small.

It is important for your child to physically use his or her finger to create a finger space. He or she also needs to reread his or her written work. That way, your child can understand why the spaces are necessary.

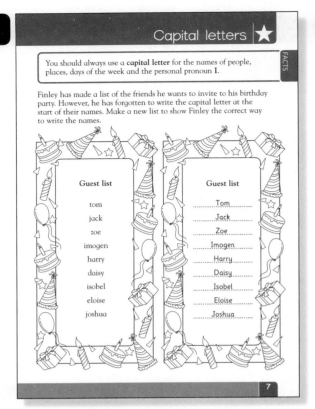

FACTS: You should always use a **capital letter** for the names of people, places, days of the week and the personal pronoun **I**.

Finley has made a list of the friends he wants to invite to his birthday party. However, he has forgotten to write the capital letter at the start of their names. Make a new list to show Finley the correct way to write the names.

Guest list

tom
jack
zoe
imogen
harry
daisy
isobel
eloise
joshua

Guest list

Tom
Jack
Zoe
Imogen
Harry
Daisy
Isobel
Eloise
Joshua

Ask your child to make a list of children he or she knows, plays with at school or wishes to invite to his or her next birthday party. Remind your child to use a capital letter for each friend's name.

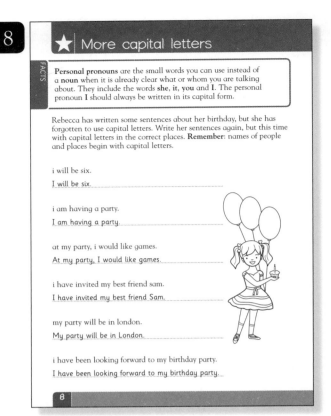

FACTS: **Personal pronouns** are the small words you can use instead of a **noun** when it is already clear what or whom you are talking about. They include the words **she**, **it**, **you** and **I**. The personal pronoun **I** should always be written in its capital form.

Rebecca has written some sentences about her birthday, but she has forgotten to use capital letters. Write her sentences again, but this time with capital letters in the correct places. **Remember:** names of people and places begin with capital letters.

i will be six.
I will be six.

i am having a party.
I am having a party.

at my party, i would like games.
At my party, I would like games.

i have invited my best friend sam.
I have invited my best friend Sam.

my party will be in london.
My party will be in London.

i have been looking forward to my birthday party.
I have been looking forward to my birthday party.

Encourage your child to spot capital letters in his or her everyday life, such as in magazines and on food packaging, signs and notices.

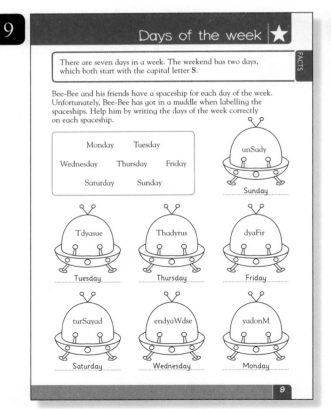

FACTS: There are seven days in a week. The weekend has two days, which both start with the capital letter **S**.

Bee-Bee and his friends have a spaceship for each day of the week. Unfortunately, Bee-Bee has got in a muddle when labelling the spaceships. Help him by writing the days of the week correctly on each spaceship.

Monday Tuesday
Wednesday Thursday Friday
Saturday Sunday

unSady — Sunday
Tdyasue — Tuesday
Thadyrus — Thursday
dyaFir — Friday
turSayad — Saturday
endyaWdse — Wednesday
yadonM — Monday

Encourage your child to tell you which day of the week it is. You can also ask questions such as "What day was it yesterday?" Remind him or her to use a capital letter whenever writing the names of the days of the week.

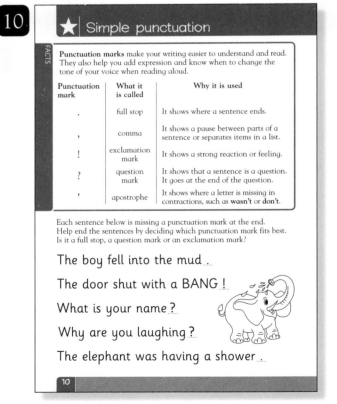

FACTS: **Punctuation marks** make your writing easier to understand and read. They also help you add expression and know when to change the tone of your voice when reading aloud.

Punctuation mark	What it is called	Why it is used
.	full stop	It shows where a sentence ends.
,	comma	It shows a pause between parts of a sentence or separates items in a list.
!	exclamation mark	It shows a strong reaction or feeling.
?	question mark	It shows that a sentence is a question. It goes at the end of the question.
'	apostrophe	It shows where a letter is missing in contractions, such as **wasn't** or **don't**.

Each sentence below is missing a punctuation mark at the end. Help end the sentences by deciding which punctuation mark fits best. Is it a full stop, a question mark or an exclamation mark?

The boy fell into the mud .

The door shut with a BANG !

What is your name ?

Why are you laughing ?

The elephant was having a shower .

When reading with or to your child, encourage him or her to spot and name punctuation marks. You could even show how punctuation should be used by changing the tone of your voice when reading a question.

More punctuation ★

A simple sentence ends with a **full stop**; a **question** ends with a **question mark**; and an **exclamation mark** shows excitement.

Maisie the Monster isn't very good at using punctuation. Look at the letter she has written to Marlon and underline the letters that should be capital letters. Then, using the table on the opposite page, add the missing punctuation marks where necessary.

246 maddison close
chichester
west sussex
england

dear marlon,

thank you for the letter! i've enjoyed reading all about what you have been doing. i have also been cooking. my favourite cake is chocolate. what is your favourite type of cake? it has been raining here since tuesday and i am fed up with not being able to go outside and play. i do like jumping in muddy puddles, just like you do. splish, splash, splosh!

i hope to see you soon.

love,
maisie

Encourage your child to spot punctuation marks and the use of capital letters in every correspondence that he or she receives. These might be party invites or letters from school.

★ Commas

In a sentence, **commas** can be used to separate words in a list. Using commas makes the list easier to read as it allows you to take a short breath between reading each word.

Look at the sentences below and add the commas in the correct places. **Remember:** we do not use a comma before the word **and** in a list.

We saw some giraffes, penguins, tigers and red pandas at the zoo.

Imogen likes pizza, pasta, curry and cake.

My friend Zoe has two cats, a fish, two chickens and a dog.

A police officer needs a notebook, a pencil and a pair of handcuffs.

Now make a list of your own, such as your pets or favourite sports, putting the commas in the correct places.

Answers may vary

Ask your child to help you make a shopping list. Remind him or her to use commas between the items on the list.

Plurals ★

When **nouns** are **singular**, there is just one of them, such as **a house**. When nouns are **plural**, there are more than one of them, such as **five foxes**. In English, we usually create the plural by adding **s** to the end. However, sometimes we add **es**. Adding **es** happens most often when the singular word ends with **s, ss, x, ch** or **sh**.

Circle the correct plural word for each of the singular words below.

dog — (dogs) or doges

flower — floweres or (flowers)

church — (churches) or churchs

brush — brushs or (brushes)

car — (cars) or cares

box — (boxes) or boxs

Now see if you can think of some singular words on your own and their plurals.

Answers may vary

Challenge your child to find examples of plural nouns used for everyday things. Ask your child to name the singular form of each of these words.

★ Irregular plurals

For **singular nouns** that end in **f** or **fe**, there are two rules to remember when making them **plural**.

If the word ends in a single **f**, you usually change **f** to **v** and add **es**.

For example:

scarf

scarves

If the word ends in **fe**, change **fe** to **ves**.

For example:

wife

wives

Read the sentences below carefully and circle the irregular plurals.

There was one wolf.
Now there are lots of (wolves).

There was one knife on the table.
Now there are lots of (knives) on the table.

There was once an elf.
All his friends were (elves), too.

The cake has been cut in half, making two (halves).

Challenge your child to think of other nouns that follow these two rules for changing the singular into the plural form.

Adding "ing" ★

FACTS

The letters **ing** are a common ending, or **suffix**, to words.
If the **root word** has a short **vowel** sound and more than one **consonant** after it, then just add **ing**.

Add **ing** to each word to make an action word.
The first one has been done for you.

Root word		Suffix		
stand	+	ing	=	standing
stick	+	ing	=	sticking
back	+	ing	=	backing
jump	+	ing	=	jumping
bless	+	ing	=	blessing
rock	+	ing	=	rocking
lift	+	ing	=	lifting

Keep an eye out for words ending in **ing** in everyday life and in any text that your child reads. Ask your child to name the root words of those words.

★ More adding "ing"

FACTS

If a **root word** has a short **vowel** with only one consonant after it, then you must **double** the consonant when adding **ing**.

Add **ing** to each word to complete the word sums.
The first one has been done for you.

Root word		Suffix		
skip	+	ing	=	skipping
beg	+	ing	=	begging
hit	+	ing	=	hitting
hug	+	ing	=	hugging
put	+	ing	=	putting
lap	+	ing	=	lapping
nod	+	ing	=	nodding
sit	+	ing	=	sitting

Encourage your child to find examples in which doubling the consonant is necessary before adding **ing**. You may need to remind your child of the rule outlined in the Facts box on this page.

Nouns ★

FACTS

A **noun** names a person, a place or a thing. A **common noun** is a general name for something, such as **dog** or **house**. A **proper noun** names a specific person or place, such as **Oliver** or **Cornwall**.

On the washing line, there are many pairs of trousers.
Colour the trousers that have a noun written on them.

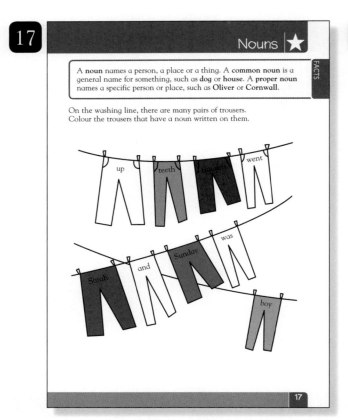

Point out more nouns to your child in everyday life. This will help familiarise him or her with the correct grammatical terms. You can then ask your child to share more examples with you.

★ Expanded noun phrases

FACTS

When we want to add description to a noun, such as **book**, we can use adjectives or groups of words that give extra information about the noun. For example: **the red book**, **an old, dusty book** and **my favourite book on the shelf** are all **expanded noun phrases** describing the noun **book**.

Read the poem below and then circle the expanded noun phrases.
The first one has been done for you.

Bo-Bo the crazy alien went one day
To a distant planet far away.
With him went his best friend Zag
And they packed a jumbo travelling bag.

Use alliteration to expand the information about each of these nouns.
You can choose words from the box below to help you.

silly	slippery	setting	slimy	shining	smelly

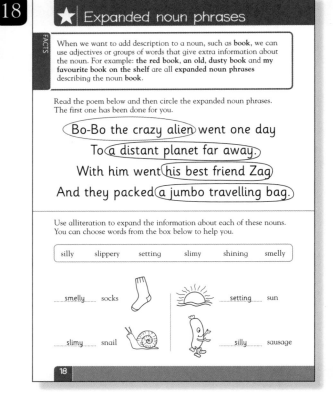

smelly socks

setting sun

slimy snail

silly sausage

This page will encourage vocabulary extension and development. When your child is talking to you, ask him or her to add more detail and description to the subject he or she is talking about.

19 — Collective nouns ★

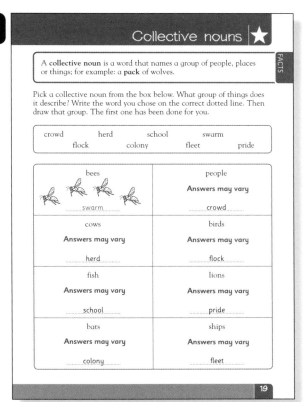

FACTS A **collective noun** is a word that names a group of people, places or things; for example: a **pack** of wolves.

Pick a collective noun from the box below. What group of things does it describe? Write the word you chose on the correct dotted line. Then draw that group. The first one has been done for you.

crowd	herd	school	swarm	
	flock	colony	fleet	pride

bees	people
swarm	**Answers may vary** crowd
cows **Answers may vary** herd	birds **Answers may vary** flock
fish **Answers may vary** school	lions **Answers may vary** pride
bats **Answers may vary** colony	ships **Answers may vary** fleet

19

Help your child come up with some collective nouns for animals and objects. You could ask him or her to think of an animal or object first and then think of what the collective noun might be.

20 — ★ Pronouns

FACTS **Pronouns** are words that can take the place of nouns in a sentence. Examples include **she**, **you**, **my** and **their**.

Circle the pronoun in each sentence.

The dog ate (my) shoe.

(They) are all going to the park.

Eleanor wore (her) best dress.

Where are (you) going?

(We) are going on holiday.

(I) like to eat chocolate.

(He) bought some new trainers.

Write three sentences of your own that include pronouns.

Answers may vary

20

To reinforce the second activity, ask your child to read aloud the three sentences he or she has written and then tell you which of the words are pronouns.

21 — Homophones ★

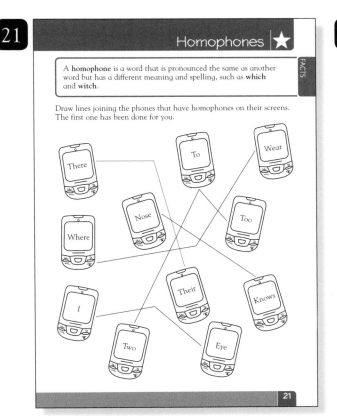

FACTS A **homophone** is a word that is pronounced the same as another word but has a different meaning and spelling, such as **which** and **witch**.

Draw lines joining the phones that have homophones on their screens. The first one has been done for you.

21

Talk to your child about other homophones and point them out when they are used during regular conversation. Tell your child the spelling used for each word.

22 — ★ More homophones

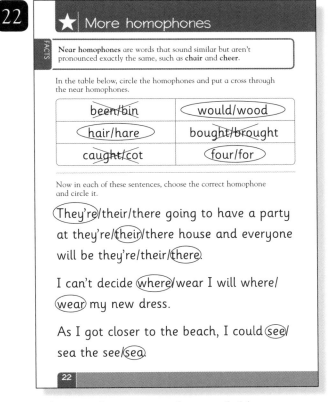

FACTS **Near homophones** are words that sound similar but aren't pronounced exactly the same, such as **chair** and **cheer**.

In the table below, circle the homophones and put a cross through the near homophones.

been/bin	would/wood
(hair/hare)	bought/brought
caught/cot	(four/for)

Now in each of these sentences, choose the correct homophone and circle it.

(They're)/their/there going to have a party at they're/(their)/there house and everyone will be they're/their/(there).

I can't decide (where)/wear I will where/ (wear) my new dress.

As I got closer to the beach, I could (see)/ sea the see/(sea).

22

When reading to or with your child, point out any near homophones you spot. Also, correct your child if he or she makes errors with near homophones in conversation.

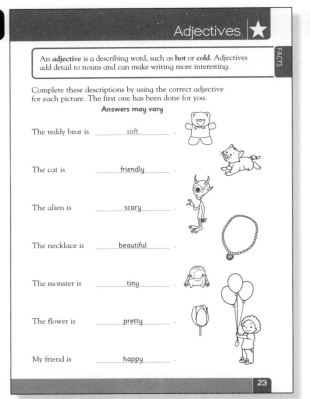

Adjectives ★

An **adjective** is a describing word, such as **hot** or **cold**. Adjectives add detail to nouns and can make writing more interesting.

Complete these descriptions by using the correct adjective for each picture. The first one has been done for you.

Answers may vary

The teddy bear is _____ soft _____ .

The cat is _____ friendly _____ .

The alien is _____ scary _____ .

The necklace is _____ beautiful _____ .

The monster is _____ tiny _____ .

The flower is _____ pretty _____ .

My friend is _____ happy _____ .

23

Ask your child to add adjectives to describe everyday objects that he or she might be talking about. Alternatively, point to objects around the home and ask your child to use an adjective to describe each one.

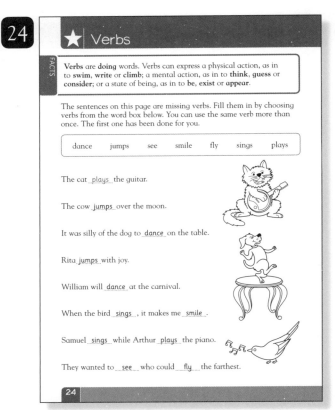

★ Verbs

Verbs are **doing** words. Verbs can express a physical action, as in to **swim**, **write** or **climb**; a mental action, as in to **think**, **guess** or **consider**; or a state of being, as in to **be**, **exist** or **appear**.

The sentences on this page are missing verbs. Fill them in by choosing verbs from the word box below. You can use the same verb more than once. The first one has been done for you.

| dance | jumps | see | smile | fly | sings | plays |

The cat _plays_ the guitar.

The cow _jumps_ over the moon.

It was silly of the dog to _dance_ on the table.

Rita _jumps_ with joy.

William will _dance_ at the carnival.

When the bird _sings_ , it makes me _smile_ .

Samuel _sings_ while Arthur _plays_ the piano.

They wanted to _see_ who could _fly_ the farthest.

24

Practise using verbs with your child by saying aloud a verb, such as **wave** or **saw**, that he or she then has to demonstrate or mime. You could also demonstrate or mime a verb that your child then has to guess.

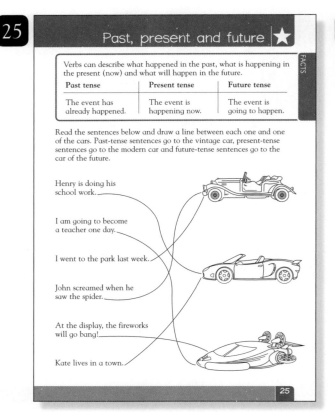

Past, present and future ★

Verbs can describe what happened in the past, what is happening in the present (now) and what will happen in the future.

Past tense	Present tense	Future tense
The event has already happened.	The event is happening now.	The event is going to happen.

Read the sentences below and draw a line between each one and one of the cars. Past-tense sentences go to the vintage car, present-tense sentences go to the modern car and future-tense sentences go to the car of the future.

Henry is doing his school work.

I am going to become a teacher one day.

I went to the park last week.

John screamed when he saw the spider.

At the display, the fireworks will go bang!

Kate lives in a town.

25

Ask your child to describe the previous day's activities using verbs in the past tense. Then, ask your child what he or she is doing now. Finally, ask what may happen tomorrow using verbs in the future tense.

★ Past tense

Verbs in the **past tense** name an action that has already happened. Some verbs can be changed to the past tense by adding **ed** to the end.

Read the letter Marlon the Monster has written to his friend Maisie. Pick the correct verbs from the box below to fill in the blanks.

| baked | jumped | tasted | skipped |
| played | helped | walked | |

Dear Maisie,

I had a busy day yesterday! First, my mum and I _baked_ a cake. It _tasted_ really nice. Then my dad and I went outside and I _jumped_ in muddy puddles, which was great fun! After that, as we _walked_ home, it started to rain hard. So we put the umbrella up and _skipped_ the rest of the way. When we got home, we _played_ a game. Finally, I _helped_ my mum make tea.

I hope you've had a good day, too!

Love,
Marlon
xxx

26

Ask your child to think how statements in the present tense might change to become statements in the past tense.

Present tense ★

Verbs in the **present tense** name an action that is happening now.

Marlon is in a muddle with his present-tense verbs. Help him complete his sentences by choosing the correct verb from the box below.

| drinks | likes | write | buy | send | see | fly |

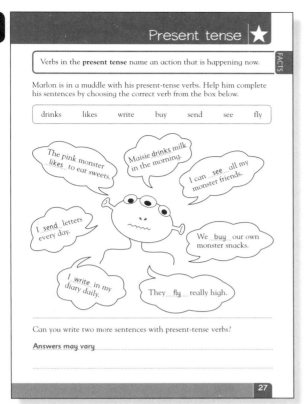

The pink monster <u>likes</u> to eat sweets.

Maisie <u>drinks</u> milk in the morning.

I can <u>see</u> all my monster friends.

I <u>send</u> letters every day.

We <u>buy</u> our own monster snacks.

I <u>write</u> in my diary daily.

They <u>fly</u> really high.

Can you write two more sentences with present-tense verbs?

<u>Answers may vary</u>

27

Ask your child to make up some statements, first using the past tense and then changing the verbs into the present tense.

★ Future tense

We use the **future tense** when an action has not already happened, nor is happening now, but will happen later.

Complete each sentence by choosing the correct verb from the box below. **Remember**: in the future tense, verbs are usually paired with **will** or **shall**.

| ride | help | go | meet | play | take | invite |

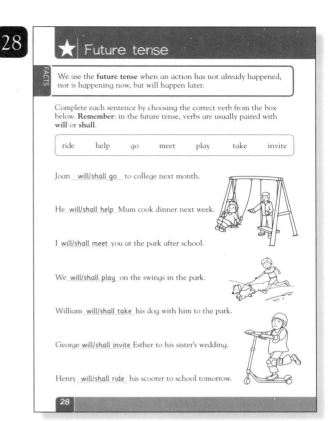

Joan <u>will/shall go</u> to college next month.

He <u>will/shall help</u> Mum cook dinner next week.

I <u>will/shall meet</u> you at the park after school.

We <u>will/shall play</u> on the swings in the park.

William <u>will/shall take</u> his dog with him to the park.

George <u>will/shall invite</u> Esther to his sister's wedding.

Henry <u>will/shall ride</u> his scooter to school tomorrow.

28

Ask your child to talk about what he or she hopes to do in the future using the correct tense.

Connectives ★

We can make longer sentences from simple sentences by using a **connective**. A connective is a word that joins two simple sentences together to make one long sentence. Two very common connectives are **and** and **but**. We use **and** when we expect the second part of a sentence to follow the first part. We use **but** when we do not expect the second part to follow the first part.

Make these pairs of short sentences into one longer sentence by choosing the connective word (**and** or **but**) that fits best. Write the new extended sentence below each pair. Add a comma before **but**, do not add it before **and**.

It was a lovely day. We enjoyed our picnic.
<u>It was a lovely day and we enjoyed our picnic.</u>

It was getting dark. Zoe wasn't frightened.
<u>It was getting dark, but Zoe wasn't frightened.</u>

Ethan and Rowan got up late. They got to school on time.
<u>Ethan and Rowan got up late, but they got to school on time.</u>

The baby giggled. She smiled at me.
<u>The baby giggled and she smiled at me.</u>

I bumped my head. It didn't hurt.
<u>I bumped my head, but it didn't hurt.</u>

Alena got a new dress. She wore her old one.
<u>Alena got a new dress, but she wore her old one.</u>

29

Ask your child to come up with a sentence using the connectives from this page. You could also throw in other connectives, such as **so** and **because**.

★ Contractions

A **contraction** is a shortened form of one or two words. In a contraction, an **apostrophe** takes the place of the missing letter or letters. For example: I am → I'm and you are → you're.

Help Elfed, the contraction wizard, choose the correct potion to make the right contractions. Colour the two bottles of potion the wizard needs to make the word on the cauldron.

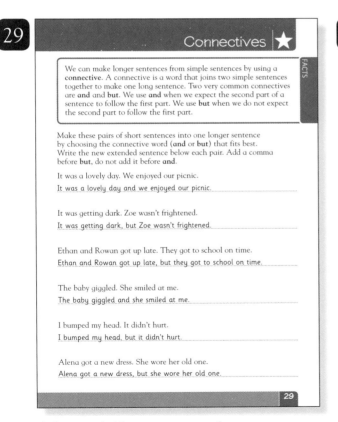

Can you think of any other contractions?
<u>Answers may vary</u>

30

When your child is writing a contracted form of any word, point out the need for an apostrophe. You could also ask him or her to identify the letter or letters the apostrophe is replacing.

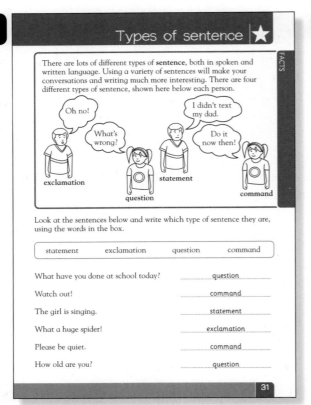

FACTS

There are lots of different types of **sentence**, both in spoken and written language. Using a variety of sentences will make your conversations and writing much more interesting. There are four different types of sentence, shown here below each person.

Oh no!

What's wrong?

I didn't text my dad.

Do it now then!

exclamation

question

statement

command

Look at the sentences below and write which type of sentence they are, using the words in the box.

| statement | exclamation | question | command |

What have you done at school today?	question
Watch out!	command
The girl is singing.	statement
What a huge spider!	exclamation
Please be quiet.	command
How old are you?	question

Talk to your child about the types of sentence he or she uses in everyday conversations. You could also encourage him or her to think about how these different sentences might be punctuated.

FACTS

It is important to learn how to spell words, especially as many common words are not pronounced exactly as they are spelled.

Read each column of these very common words.
Next, cover the words up one by one and write them down on the dotted lines.

again	again	little	little
all	all	much	much
over	over	what	what
took	took	him	him
very	very	open	open
want	want	everyone	everyone
yes	yes	sister	sister
some	some	our	our
there	there	people	people
down	down	up	up
school	school	because	because
just	just	come	come

This page will help your child spell these words confidently. Encourage your child to read each word slowly and carefully. Ensure that he or she writes the words clearly in the spaces given.

Glossary

Alliteration
A way of writing in which the same sound or letter is used at the beginning of each or most of the words in a phrase or a sentence. For example: **the setting sun was a sight to see.**

Alphabet
The 26 letters we use to make words.

Connective
A word such as **and** or **but** that joins two or more parts in a sentence.

Consonants
The 21 letters of the alphabet that are not vowels. The letter **y** can be both a vowel (as in **myth**) and a consonant (as in **yet**).

Letter
A symbol used to write a speech sound. For example: **Aa, Bb, Cc** and so on are letters of the alphabet.

Noun
A word for an object, a place or a person. For example: **John, field, girl, school** and **chair**.

Plural
A word that refers to more than one of something. We usually, but not always, just add an **s** to the singular. For example: **tigers** (tiger), **books** (book) and **lives** (life).

Pronoun
A word that can take the place of a noun in a sentence. Pronouns include **my, he, her, your, their** and **itself.**

Pronunciation
A particular way of saying a word.

Root word
A root word contains the essential, or main, meaning of a word. Prefixes and suffixes are often added to root words. For example, **park** is the root word of **parking**.

Sentence
A group of words that are linked together to give a specific meaning. For example: **I am packing my bags**.

Singular
A word that refers to a single person or thing, such as a **boy**, an **apple** or one **chair.**

Suffix
A group of letters added to the end of a root word to make a new word. For example: the root word **smile** and the suffix **ing** make **smiling**.

Vowels
The letters **a, e, i, o** and **u**. The letter **y** is often used as a vowel, too.

Word
A particular set of letters, such as **white, boat, desk** or **dry**, that has a meaning of its own.